The Birth of Ben Nevis

and the story behind Lochaber's landscape

Edited by Noel Williams

With contributions from

Alison Austin, Jim Blair, Julian Bukits, Rob Gill, Keith Hoole,

David Jarman, Adrian Palmer, Ian Parsons and Noel Williams

Lochaber Geopark

www.lochabergeopark.org.uk

First published in Great Britain by Lochaber Geopark 2010
Copyright © Lochaber Geopark 2010

ISBN 978-0-9565369-0-7

Diagrams: Noel Williams, Felicity Nightingale, Scottish Natural Heritage
Maps: Ashworth Maps and Interpretation Ltd and British Geological Survey
Photos: Lochaber Geopark Directors, Alex Gillespie (p9 top), Highland Council
(p19 top & bottom), David Jarman (pp 26 top, 27), National Museum of Scotland
(p35 bottom), English Heritage (p42) and British Geological Survey (p44)
Graphic Design: Wagtail Graphics

Typeset and printed by PrintSmith, Fort William

Front cover: Ben Nevis viewed from Cow Hill above Fort William
Photo: Noel Williams

Geology in action!
This landslide took place on
the flank of Meall an t-Suidhe
on Saturday 6th March 2010
in full view of the crowd
watching a shinty match in
Fort William. Countless events
like this in the past were
responsible for creating the
vast quantities of scree seen
on the the local mountains.
Photo © Oban Times.

Contents

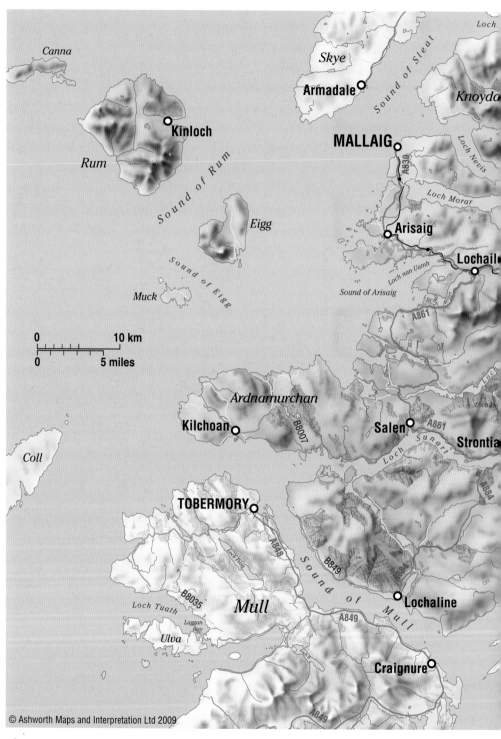

Canna

Kinloch

Rum

Sound of Rum

Eigg

Sound of Eigg

Muck

Sound of Arisaig

Skye

Armadale

Sound of Sleat

Knoyda

MALLAIG

A838

Loch Nevis

Loch Morar

Arisaig

Lochail

Loch nan Uamh

A861

Loch

Ardnamurchan

Kilchoan

B8007

Salen

A861

Strontia

Loch Sunart

A884

Coll

TOBERMORY

Loch Frisa

A848

Sound

B849

A884

Loch Do

B8035

Mull

Loch Tuath

Laggan Bay

Ulva

A849

of

Mull

Lochaline

Craignure

A849

© Ashworth Maps and Interpretation Ltd 2009

0 ⊢ 10 km
0 ⊢ 5 miles

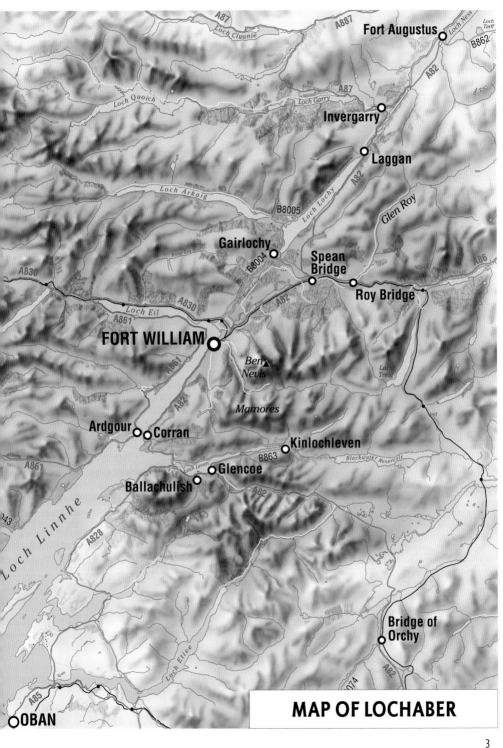

MAP OF LOCHABER

3

The Geology of Ben Nevis

Noel Williams

Ben Nevis is not only Britain's highest mountain it is also a spectacular example of a deeply eroded caldera volcano. The rocks now forming the summit of Ben Nevis have only survived erosion because they collapsed into a chamber of molten granite magma some 410 million years ago.

An ascent of Ben Nevis is a fairly demanding undertaking, especially if you're not normally an active hillwalker. So to help take your mind off all the exertion look at the rocks under your feet as you climb to the highest point in the British Isles, 1344m (4408ft) above sea level.

A walk into a caldera

The first part of the path from Achintee crosses glacial moraine and no bedrock is exposed. However, a short distance after crossing a stile, some 600m from Achintee, there is a small outcrop of metamorphic rock on the east side of the path. It was originally an impure limestone but was strongly affected by heat from the Ben Nevis granite and was changed into a pale-green and white banded rock called **hornfels**; the pale green colour is due to the presence of a mineral called tremolite.

Soon after this the path crosses onto **quartz-diorite** – the outermost of the Ben Nevis intrusions. This rock is similar to granite, but is grey in colour and has rather less quartz. There are numerous exposures of it beside the path.

The next change in rock type occurs where the path from the Youth Hostel joins the main path. Here the rock is a very coarse-grained granite known as the **Ben**

Nevis Outer Granite. This rock also forms the summit of neighbouring Aonach Mòr. It has the largest vertical thickness (1200m) of any granitic rock exposed in the UK. As the path ascends through two sets of zigzags it is possible to see several **dykes** cutting through the granite. These narrow intrusions are finer-grained and slightly darker than the granite. They were formed when magma was injected into vertical fractures which formed in the granite after it had cooled. They trend in a NE–SW direction. These dykes

are completely absent from the inner granite.

There is also a conspicuous dark-coloured dyke clearly visible in the path between the two aluminium bridges. However, this trends in a completely different direction to the others (WNW–ESE). This is because it is a much younger basalt dyke which can be linked to the volcanic activity that occurred on Skye around 60 million years ago. It shows very obvious spheroidal or 'onion-skin' weathering.

Shortly before the path zigzags towards Lochan Meall

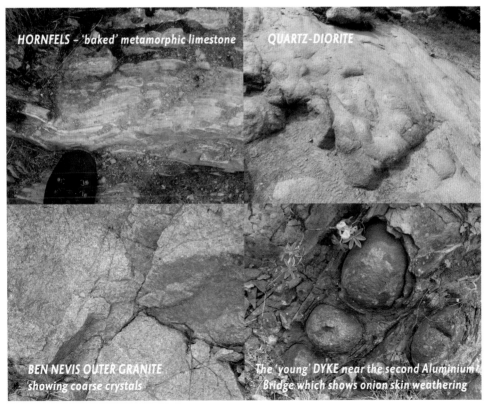

HORNFELS – 'baked' metamorphic limestone

QUARTZ-DIORITE

BEN NEVIS OUTER GRANITE showing coarse crystals

The 'young' DYKE near the second Aluminium Bridge which shows onion skin weathering

Inside the Ben Nevis caldera!
On the upper part of the mountain the path
lies on a collapsed pile of ANDESITE lavas

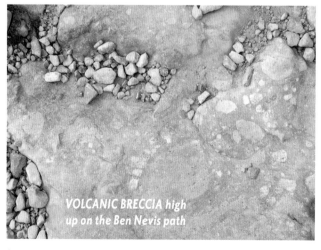

VOLCANIC BRECCIA *high*
up on the Ben Nevis path

an t-Suidhe the rock changes again to the much redder **Ben Nevis Inner Granite**. This rock is easily seen where the path cuts southwards and crosses the 'Red Burn'. The rock is also obvious on the first three legs of the major zigzags which ascend the western flank of the mountain.

Then, just by the third corner of these zigzags, the path moves onto a very different dark grey coloured rock. This is the start of the great pile of volcanic rocks – mainly **andesite lavas** – which form all the upper section of the mountain. They represent the remains of the huge cylindrical block – around 2km across – which sank into the granite whilst it was still molten. In some samples the rock is speckled with small light-coloured crystals of feldspar.

Where separate angular blocks of various sizes can be distinguished within the rock it is known as **volcanic breccia**. This material was produced during more explosive eruptions.

The most remarkable feature of the upper plateau of Ben Nevis is the **blockfield** which everywhere covers the ground. This coating of boulders was created when the upper part of the mountain experienced prolonged freeze-thaw action. This happened during the last glaciation when ice sheets were less extensive and the highest peaks remained exposed above the ice as nunataks. Previous coverings of blockfield would have been removed when the summits were completely buried by a major ice sheet.

If you're lucky enough to get a good view at the summit you should be able to see that the mountains which neighbour Ben Nevis are built of different coloured rocks. Càrn Mòr Dearg is made of red Inner Granite, whilst Aonach Mòr is made of slightly paler Outer Granite. Most of the other nearby mountains are built of metamorphic rocks such as mica schist (e.g. Aonach Beag) or white quartzite (e.g. Sgùrr a' Mhaim and Stob Ban).

You may feel elated to have made it to the highest point in Britain, but bear in mind that the rocks forming the summit of Ben Nevis would once have been well over 600m (2000ft) higher

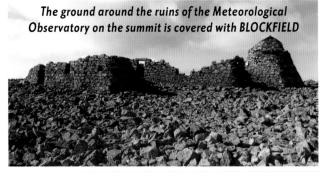

The ground around the ruins of the Meteorological Observatory on the summit is covered with BLOCKFIELD

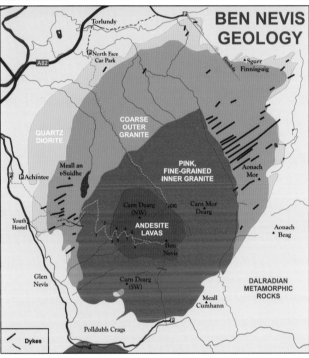

BEN NEVIS GEOLOGY

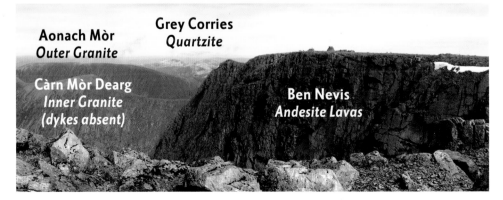

Aonach Mòr
Outer Granite

Grey Corries
Quartzite

Càrn Mòr Dearg
Inner Granite
(dykes absent)

Ben Nevis
Andesite Lavas

The sequence of events which created Ben Nevis

1. Around 410 million years ago a volcano erupts onto a land surface of metamorphic rocks (eroded Caledonian mountains). Initial deposits, which include volcanic breccia, are covered by numerous andesite lava flows.

2. The lavas fill in a depression in the landscape. Some of the ash falls settle into freshwater lochans.

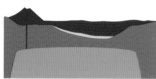

3. A large body of magma rises within the crust.

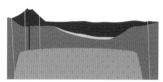

4. The magma cools and crystallises to form the OUTER GRANITE. The area is then subjected to sideways tension. Vertical fractures develop in the crust and molten material is erupted to the surface along these fissures to create dykes.

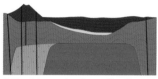

5. The dykes cool and crystallise. Some time later a new body of magma rises within the crust.

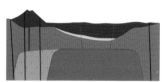

6. Pressure from the new magma domes up the roof of the magma chamber. When the magma subsides slightly the roof can no longer support itself and a cylindrical fracture develops.

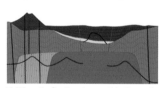

7. When the fracture is complete the roof starts to fail. (The wavy black lines mark the present day land surface.)

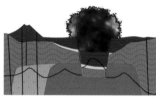

8. A cylindrical block starts to sink down into the magma chamber. Vast quantities of gas and hot ash escape around the margins of the sinking block.

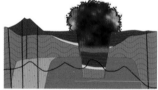

9. A CALDERA is formed at the surface and fresh lavas are erupted into this giant crater.

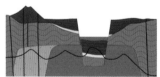

10. Eventually volcanic activity ceases. The magma then cools and crystallises to form the INNER GRANITE.

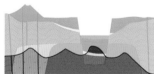

11. Over the next 100 million years huge quantities of rock are removed by erosion. In the succeeding 250 million years large parts of the Highlands are at times submerged by the sea.

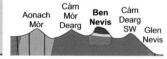

12. Renewed uplift of the Scottish Highlands began some 50 million years ago. Repeated glaciations over the last 2 million years have shaped the landscape we see today.

 VOLCANIC BRECCIA

 OUTER GRANITE

 INNER GRANITE

 SCHIST and other metamorphic rocks

 ANDESITE LAVA

 DYKE

The original position of the rocks before the collapse of the Ben Nevis caldera

600m (2000ft)

Photo © Alex Gillespie

North Face of Ben Nevis

than they are today relative to the neighbouring peaks! Some 410 million years ago they collapsed down into a chamber of molten granite in a spectacular event which created a massive crater at the surface called a **caldera**. Huge quantities of frothy magma and hot ash would have been blasted into the atmosphere. Eventually all volcanic activity ceased.

Continual erosion has since removed a vast amount of rock. So when you're standing on the summit today you're actually directly beneath the centre of that former caldera. See step 11 in the diagram opposite.

Have a safe journey down!

If you'd like to learn a bit more about the ancient calderas in Ben Nevis and Glen Coe look for a small booklet entitled: *Ben Nevis and Glencoe - a Landscape Fashioned by Geology*, published by Scottish Natural Heritage, 2007.
ISBN 978 1 85397 506 6.

SGURR FINNISG-AIG
Quartz Diorite

AONACH MÒR
Outer Granite

CÀRN MÒR DEARG
Inner Granite

BEN NEVIS
Andesite Lavas

Meeting of Three Waters

Noel Williams

The place known as the 'Meeting of Three Waters' is situated in the floor of Glen Coe below the mouth of Coire Gabhail. As the name suggests it is a place where three different streams meet. Not very remarkable you might think, until you see the very straight courses that the streams take to their meeting place.

The River Coe flows in from the north-east and meets the Allt Coire Gabhail head on as it tumbles out of Coire Gabhail. A smaller stream called the Allt Doire-bheith joins them from the east-south-east. The water from all three streams then flows through a deep gorge.

A quick look at a map of Glen Coe reveals the curious angles at which these streams meet. They form a distinct 'cross' on the ground. You could say that X marks the spot. This shape is no accident. The streams meet in the way they do because they have eroded along two intersecting dykes, which have proved to be slightly softer than the surrounding rocks.

The story behind these dykes starts over 400 million years ago. Tension in the

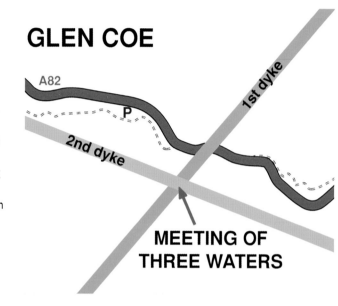

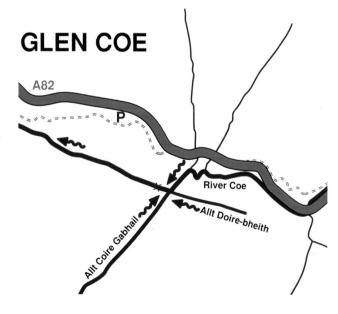

Earth's crust created a series of vertical cracks running right across the Glen Coe area. Molten material erupted into these long fissures and eventually cooled and solidified to form a large number of dykes trending in a north-east to south-west direction. This occurred round about the time that a great caldera was created in Glen Coe.

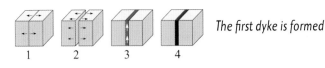

The first dyke is formed

The second dyke is formed

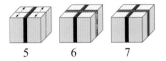

The dykes are softer than the surrounding rocks and so are picked out by erosion

Much later on – about 300 million years ago – the area was pulled apart in a different direction and a smaller number of dykes were formed running east-south-east to west-north-west.

The footpath which leads up into Coire Gabhail (commonly called the Lost Valley) crosses the River Coe by a footbridge over a gorge about 90m downstream from the Meeting of Three Waters. Although the path then passes close to where the streams meet, it is not easy to see the junction clearly from here.

The best place to view this feature is from the flank of A' Chailleach on the north side of the main A82 road. You can also make out the huge landslide off Gearr Aonach that left a great jumble of giant blocks in the floor of Coire Gabhail after the last ice age. It also becomes clear that the whole of Coire Gabhail has been eroded along the line of the same dyke that runs across the floor of the glen.

STOB COIRE NAN LOCHAN

COIRE GABHAIL

LANDSLIDE

MEETING OF THREE WATERS

An Sgùrr – Island of Eigg

Alison Austin

One of the most distinctive sights in western Lochaber is the spectacular prow called An Sgùrr on the island of Eigg. How was this unusual feature created?

Around 200 million years ago Scotland was not as it is today. It was sandwiched in the middle of a great supercontinent called Pangea surrounded by the Americas to the west, Greenland and Scandinavia to the north and east, and England, Europe and Africa to the south.

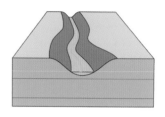

1. A river erodes a valley in a pile of basalt lavas

The surface of our planet is made up of a number of segments which geologists call tectonic plates. These plates are continually jostling and moving around on the Earth's surface. When plates collide with each other, as is happening today on the west coast of South America, ocean crust is pushed underneath continental crust. During such plate collisions earthquakes occur and mountains such as the Andes are created. Rocks start to melt at great depth and magma rises up through the crust. Where the magma escapes to the surface it erupts to form volcanoes.

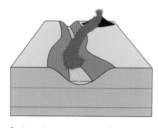

2. A violent eruption of hot ash pours into the valley

When plates split apart basalt magma wells up from deep in the Earth's crust and erupts from long fissures. On the floor of the Atlantic Ocean there is a feature known as the Mid Atlantic Ridge where two plates are spreading apart at the present day. Basalt magma continually erupts along the line of the ridge to create new ocean floor. Europe and America are moving apart at about the rate your fingernails grow. This separation began around 140 million years ago when Pangea started to break up, but it wasn't until 60 Ma that Scotland and Greenland began to split apart and the northern section of the Atlantic Ocean started to form.

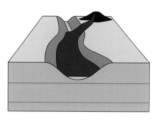

3. The flow cools to form pitchstone

Initially there were great eruptions of basalt lava. On Eigg

4. The basalt erodes more quickly than the pitchstone

these flows formed distinctive flat layers known as plateau lavas. They may have come from a centre on Mull. Long periods of time often elapsed between lava flows, time enough for soil to form and plants to grow. Before the eruptions that created An Sgùrr took place a meandering river cut a deep channel into the existing basalt lava flows.

Around 58 million years ago a rather unusual explosive type of eruption took place. A hot cloud of silica rich ash and rock fragments flowed into the river valley and solidified to form a black, glassy rock called **pitchstone**. This is the youngest volcanic eruption still preserved in Scotland.

The east face of An Sgùrr showing the contact between pitchstone and the side of the ancient river valley

As it cooled and contracted impressive columnar jointing formed within the pitchstone. The columns are similar to but narrower than those seen on Staffa.

The pitchstone cooled very quickly, just like the basalt did, but because it has a different composition to basalt it later weathered at a different rate. Over time the neighbouring basalt has eroded away more easily, and the harder pitchstone now stands proud.

Columnar jointing on An Sgùrr

The South Face of An Sgùrr

Dubh-ghlac – Onich Gorge

Jim Blair

1. *Dubh-ghlac from the main A82 road.*
2. *View up the OnichDry Gorge.*
3. *View looking down into the Dry Gorge, with the 'dun' on the hilltop to the left.*

Dubh-ghlac is a long narrow glen running north-east from the main road in Onich. Its Gaelic name means 'dark narrow glen', but it is also known as the Onich Dry River Gorge, or simply the Onich Gorge.

You can catch a glimpse of the entrance to Dubh-ghlac as you drive through Onich, but the best way to appreciate the story behind this feature is to follow the 'An Drochaid Circular Walk', starting from the Forestry Commission Car Park behind Inchree.

This walk is 6km long and takes about 2 hours to complete. It ascends by the waterfalls in the *Abhainn Righ* (River Righ) and after a couple of right turns it crosses the river by *An Drochaid* (the bridge). The path then continues across moorland above the north-western lip of the gorge, giving great views across to the oak and hazel woodland on the eastern side. An old, iron-age 'dun', or fort, lies hidden in the trees at the top of the hill, the steep slope providing a good defence from that direction. (Please take note of the 'steep cliffs' signs!)

There is only the merest trickle of a burn oozing down the marshy bottom of the gorge, and it is certainly not the sort of river one might expect to have eroded a glen of this size. The Abhainn Righ which flows strongly under the An Drochaid footbridge to the north is only about 5 meters below the level of the threshold into Dubh-ghlac. It seems likely that the river once flowed along Dubh-ghlac, before being diverted, possibly as a result of glacial action. The river now plunges down a series of spectacular waterfalls towards Inchree.

From the floor of Dubh-ghlac the steep north-westerly side of the gorge can be seen to be formed by a long exposure of white rock, over 20 meters high in places, known as Appin Quartzite.

This rock was originally deposited as a clean, white sand on the bed of an ancient sea called the Iapetus Ocean. Closure of this ocean by movements in the Earth's crust resulted in the formation of the Caledonian mountain range. Deep burial of the white sand grains squeezed them so strongly that they fused together to become the tough, metamorphic rock called quartzite.

Despite this squeezing some of the ripple marks on the old sea bed have survived and can be seen on the rock face. This is why the area is recognised as a Site of Special Scientific Interest (SSSI). What was once horizontal sea floor now dips down at an angle of 60 to 70 degrees.

Boulders of yellow-weathering limestone may be seen in the bottom of the gorge. This limestone proved to be much softer than the quartzite and so was eroded out by running water to create the gorge. From the hills above the gorge, the woodlands growing on the rich limestone areas are in strong contrast to the sparse moorland of the nutrient-poor quartzite areas.

The glen is also part of the prominent raised beach system at Onich. In fairly recent times geologically speaking, Dubh-ghlac would have been an inlet of the sea.

For details of the An Drochaid circular walk see: http://www.highland.gov.uk/leisure/countryside/countrysideaccess/pathsaroundlochaber.htm

Ancient ripple marks prominent on a steeply inclined bed of quartzite

Enjoying one of the Inchree Waterfalls

The Ardnamurchan 'Volcano'

Rob Gill

The Ardnamurchan peninsula attracts a surprisingly large number of visitors over the course of a year, surprising because it is at the end of a very beautiful, but somewhat long single track road, and not on the route to anywhere else.

That this is the most westerly point on the mainland draws many to the area, and Sanna beach is one of the finest in Scotland, but the fact that it was once a volcano is not so widely known. Anyone continuing past Kilchoan and heading to Sanna will pass through Achnaha, a small hamlet of white painted houses. This is situated at the centre of an impressive ring of crags about 3 miles across. These look for all the world like a volcanic crater, or a large collapse structure called a caldera. There is a definite feel that you are in the centre of a 'volcano'.

The description of crater or caldera is quite correct for the spectacular view you see today. There would have been both at some stage 60 million years ago, when the volcano was active. A typical cone-shaped volcano would, in all probability, have towered one or two miles above the present day land surface! Where has all this gone?

Anyone lucky enough to have visited an active volcano is struck by the insubstantial nature of what he is standing on. Most volcanoes seem to consist of the sort of thing left in the grate after a coal fire the night before – loose ash. Many volcanic cones are for the most part just great piles of loose ash. They are not very stable, and erode very rapidly. Mud slides after heavy rain (known as lahars) are very common, and dangerous if

Sanna Bay

you happen to be in the way.

There were three volcanoes in Ardnamurchan, one a mile or so to the east, one a similar distance to the west. Geologists have plotted their rise and fall, but the last one centred near Achnaha has obliterated a good part of the earlier ones, leaving only their outer edges as proof of their existence.

All this volcanic activity came about as Scotland and Greenland started to separate from each other as the North Atlantic Ocean was created. Even today we are still very slowly moving away from Greenland. A rift which runs right across Iceland marks where the split is taking place.

What you can see today in Ardnamurchan is the heart of an ancient volcano, once deep underground. Molten, but never erupted, the rock cooled slowly to form gabbro, a hard, dark rock with large crystals. The outer part is of slightly different composition, and more resistant to erosion

Ardnamurchan Lighthouse

than the rocks at the centre.

The final chapter in the formation of the 'crater' was written in the last Ice Age. Glaciers completely covered the area. Even the tops of the hills were smoothed by ice action. More rock was scraped from the centre than from the resistant edge, and it is this that has resulted in the 'crater' visible today rather than direct volcanic activity; but the site, the shape and the 'feel' of the volcano remain for the visitors of today.

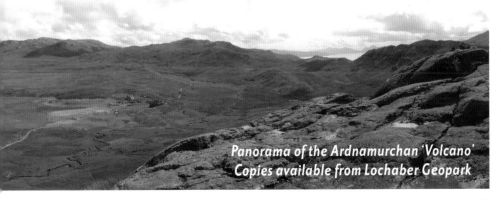

Panorama of the Ardnamurchan 'Volcano'
Copies available from Lochaber Geopark

The Great Glen   *Alison Austin*

The Great Glen is the longest glen in Scotland. It is major hollow which cuts right across the Highlands from Inverness to Fort William. The glen is remarkably straight and is part-filled by three long freshwater lochs. Thomas Telford saw the benefits of exploiting this natural feature when he built the Caledonian Canal.

Why is Scotland cut in half by such a glen and why are the lochs along its length of such amazing depth? Part of the answer lies deep in geological time for the Great Glen marks the line of an enormous geological fault.

A fault is a break in the Earth's crust where movement takes place. A modern day example of an active fault is the San Andreas fault in California. Earthquakes occur when the two crustal blocks on either side of this fault suddenly snap and slip horizontally past each other. The Great Glen Fault was once very similar. It possibly extends as far as Shetland in the north. It certainly continues in a southwesterly direction along Loch Linnhe to the south end of Mull. A branch of it may also continue across Ireland.

The Glen Glen fault has a long and very complicated history. The rocks on either side of it moved in different directions at different times. At least three different sorts of movement are believed to have taken place along the fault. The most significant movement probably occurred between 430 and 400 million years ago, when the northwest part of Scotland moved as much as 200km in a southwesterly direction relative to the rest of the country. Several smaller faults running parallel to the Great Glen were also active around this time. This is when the separate segments of crust that now make up Scotland were first assembled together.

Some time later movement took place along the fault in exactly the opposite direction. We know from the way that certain dykes are now displaced by the fault that the rocks on the north-west side slid back at least 7–8km in a north-easterly direction.

The story doesn't end

CONTINENTS COLLIDE
430 million years ago

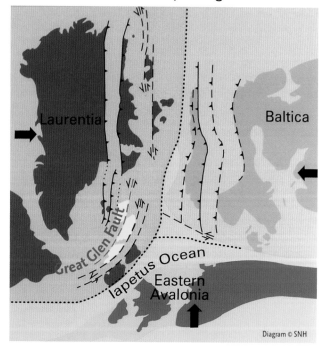

Diagram © SNH

there though. Sediments on the floor of the Moray Firth suggest that much later on the rocks on the southeast side of the fault moved vertically downwards instead of sideways.

There does not appear to be any significant movement along the fault today, although there were a number of minor earthquakes in the Inverness area just over a century ago. The largest was of magnitude 5.1 centred around Dochgarroch (7km southwest of Inverness) and took place in 1901. The shock was felt as far away as Fife. A lot of minor damage was done to buildings, and a couple of minor buildings collapsed, in one case injuring a horse.

Finally, why does the Great Glen contain such deep lochs? Loch Ness for example is 230m (750ft) deep and its floor lies well below sea level. The answer is to be found in the more recent past. For

the last 2 million years of its history the Earth has been experiencing an Ice Age where the climate has fluctuated through a series of glacial and inter-glacial periods. During glacial times ice built up on higher ground and flowed

down the Great Glen. Along the line of the Great Glen fault there is a 3km wide zone of crushed and shattered rock. The ice gouged out this softer rock more easily to create the U-shaped glen and deep lochs we see today.

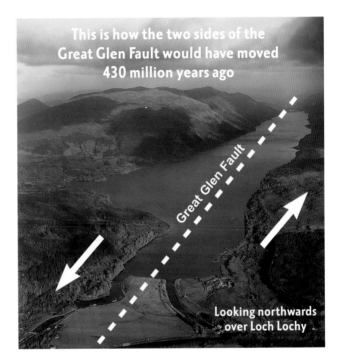

This is how the two sides of the Great Glen Fault would have moved 430 million years ago

Great Glen Fault

Looking northwards over Loch Lochy

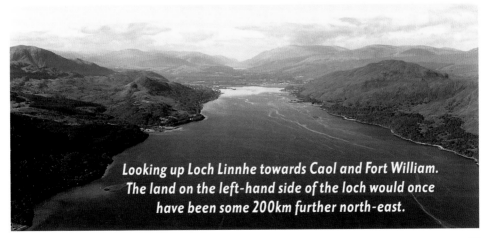

Looking up Loch Linnhe towards Caol and Fort William. The land on the left-hand side of the loch would once have been some 200km further north-east.

The Parallel Roads   *Noel Williams*

When you travel through Roy Bridge on the main A86 road you could be forgiven if you failed to realise that this is where you must turn off to visit one of Lochaber's most spectacular scenic features – The Parallel Roads. There is no signpost in the village indicating their whereabouts. Perhaps this is because the single track road up Glen Roy is not really suitable for heavy traffic. You need to venture up the glen for just over 5km before you are rewarded with a fine view of the distinctive parallel markings that have made Glen Roy famous around the world. From the carpark at the viewpoint it is possible to climb up a grassy hillside to stand on the lowest Road and if you're feeling energetic you can continue uphill to visit the two higher ones as well.

The story of how these markings were formed aroused great interest in the nineteenth century. A young Charles Darwin, fresh from his voyage to South America, thought that the Roads marked former levels of the sea. In 1840 Louis Agassiz, a Swiss geologist, suggested that glaciers had once existed in Scotland. He argued that the Roads were former shorelines of freshwater lochs created when a glacier blocked the normal exit for water draining from Glen Roy.

This was eventually accepted as the correct explanation, but it was 20 years later before a Scottish scientist, Thomas Jamieson, worked out the full sequence of events that resulted in three separate Roads being formed in Glen Roy.

It was also recognised early on that the Parallel Roads are not just confined to Glen Roy.

They are also present in Glen Gloy and Glen Spean. If you examine the Ordnance Survey map of Glen Spean you will see just how extensive the Roads are. When the tunnel was constructed for the hydro-electric scheme for the aluminium smelter in the 1920s the puggy line closely followed part of the Parallel Road on the south side of Glen Spean notably around the flank of Beinn Chlianaig.

One of the puzzling

HOW THE PARALLEL ROADS WERE FORMED

Water overflows into the Spey Valley via the 350m col at the head of Glen Roy

350m loch — GLACIER FLOWS UP INTO GLEN ROY

Water overflows via the 325m col to reach Glen Spean at Roughburn

325m loch — GLACIER MELTS BACK AND REVEALS LOWER COL

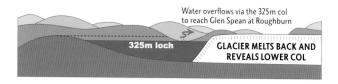

Water overflows into Strath Mashie at the 260m col 3km east of Kinloch Laggan

260m loch — GLACIER

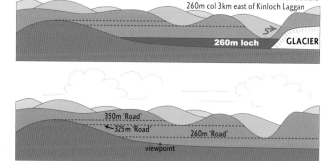

350m 'Road'
325m 'Road'
260m 'Road'
viewpoint

aspects of the glacial theory is why a glacier flowed UP into the mouth of Glen Roy. It might be expected that the glacier would flow DOWN the glen instead. The answer is rather complicated. The Earth has experienced alternating glacial and interglacial episodes over the last two million years. During some of the major glacial periods the whole country was covered in ice. At other times glaciers filled all the local glens, but the main mountain summits remained above the ice.

There was a mild episode some 14,000 years ago when temperatures were similar to today. Then a fairly short-lived glacial episode took place and by 12,500 years ago a large ice cap had developed over western Scotland. This extended from Torridon in the north to Loch Lomond in the south and was confined to the western hills because that was where precipitation was greatest.

A lobe of this ice cap spread up into Glen Spean and joined with a lobe of ice flowing northwards off Nevis Range and down the line of Loch Treig. This is when ice pushed UP into Glen Roy and Glen Gloy. In the summer months the meltwater could not escape from the glens by the normal routes because a natural dam of ice blocked the exits. The different Roads where created when the

water escaped over different cols depending on the extent of the ice.

If you visit the viewpoint in Glen Roy you have to imagine that when the glacier was at its maximum extent there would have been hundreds of feet of ice above your head. Then, when the ice started to retreat, there would have been hundreds of feet

of water above your head instead. What eventually happened to all that water is the subject of the next article.

If you would like to find out more about the Parallel Roads of Lochaber see a booklet entitled *Glen Roy – a Landscape Fashioned by Geology*, part of a series published by Scottish Natural Heritage.

The middle and upper Parallel Roads in Glen Roy

A view of lower Glen Roy from Beinn Chlianaig

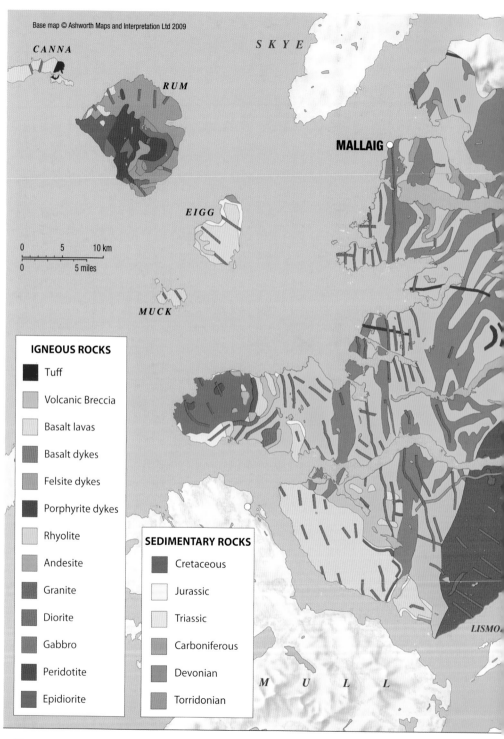

Base map © Ashworth Maps and Interpretation Ltd 2009

CANNA

RUM

SKYE

MALLAIG

EIGG

0   5   10 km

0   5 miles

MUCK

IGNEOUS ROCKS

- Tuff
- Volcanic Breccia
- Basalt lavas
- Basalt dykes
- Felsite dykes
- Porphyrite dykes
- Rhyolite
- Andesite
- Granite
- Diorite
- Gabbro
- Peridotite
- Epidiorite

SEDIMENTARY ROCKS

- Cretaceous
- Jurassic
- Triassic
- Carboniferous
- Devonian
- Torridonian

LISMO.

MULL

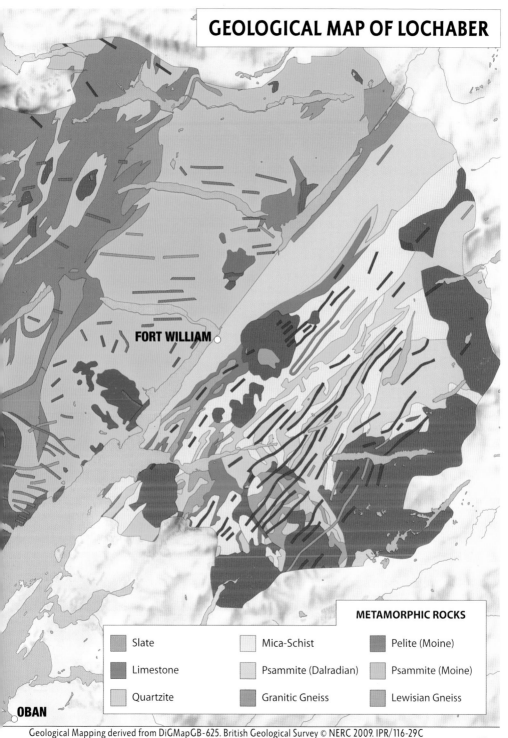

GEOLOGICAL MAP OF LOCHABER

FORT WILLIAM

OBAN

METAMORPHIC ROCKS

- Slate
- Limestone
- Quartzite
- Mica-Schist
- Psammite (Dalradian)
- Granitic Gneiss
- Pelite (Moine)
- Psammite (Moine)
- Lewisian Gneiss

Geological Mapping derived from DiGMapGB-625. British Geological Survey © NERC 2009. IPR/116-29C

The Spean Gorge   *Keith Hoole*

Where did all the water go? What water do I hear you say…

In the previous article we learned how some 12,000 years ago, during a short-lived glacial episode, an ice cap developed over western hills. Eastward flowing glaciers pushed up into the mouths of Glen Spean, Glen Roy and Glen Gloy. Large lochs were formed in these glens behind the huge natural ice dams. The famous Parallel Roads of Lochaber mark the former shorelines of these lochs.

So let's return to the original question. What happened to all the water in these lochs when the glaciers responsible for creating them started to melt?

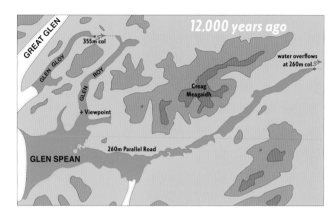

Just before the ice dam in Glen Spean started to fail there was an enormous loch in Glen Spean and a separate one in Glen Gloy – see the sketch map above. It has been estimated that 5 cubic kilometres of water were trapped in Glen Spean. Imagine pulling the plug on such a massive bath.

It is thought that when the water started to escape it did so beneath the ice. As the flow increased the pressure of water soon created a great tunnel through which a vast quantity of water and debris poured. The water, carried with it sand, gravel, boulders and chunks of ice. It rapidly wore away the bed of the glacier and the ice of the glacier itself. There is a wonderful Icelandic word *jökulhlaup* (meaning 'glacier burst'), used to describe such a dramatic escape of water from beneath a glacier.

There would have been at least two separate jökulhlaups in Lochaber – one from Glen Spean and another from Glen Gloy. The escaping water tore at the underlying rock and soil and ripped it away to create a deep gorge beneath the ice.

Looking down the Gloy Gorge towards Loch Lochy

It is possible to imagine the power involved in this event by examining the channel cut into solid rock in the Spean Gorge downstream from Spean Bridge. It is particularly impressive between Highbridge and Gairlochy. There is a similar gorge in the River Gloy just beside the A82.

The escaping water would have rushed on into Loch Lochy. But the way south to Loch Linnhe was still blocked by ice, so the flood water had to turn north-east past Fort Augustus and on into Loch Ness. A great pulse of water would have continued along Loch Ness and this would have created a huge tidal wave in the shallower section at Lochend. This threw up a vast amount of sand and gravel which now extends well out into the Moray Firth and has created a flat expanse of well-drained ground on which much of Inverness is built. This was the largest recorded freshwater flood Scotland has ever known.

As one Glen Roy resident put it when told of the story: "Ach it seems it's always been that way; everything goes to Inverness. I thought that it was just the poor crofter's money, but now it seems that they even stole the soil from under our feet as well!"

Looking upstream in the Spean Gorge

Looking downstream in the Spean Gorge

Looking across the Spean Gorge towards Nevis Range

Knoydart's split mountain

David Jarman

If you go up into the Alps, you might well come across a curious phenomenon – a mountain crest with another one running along beside it, sometimes lower, sometimes higher. In German they are called *doppelgrats*, and rather like shadowy doppelgangers in ghost stories, they can be spooky in swirling mists, when you wonder which is the true ridge, and where to go now, or are you seeing double?

The twin summit ridges of Aonach Sgoilte viewed from the east

Direction of slip

How they are made is quite simple really – a fracture develops along one side of the crest, a little way down, which slants into the mountainside, and comes out much further down the other side. Then the summit ridge starts to creep and slip down it. Sometimes it disintegrates as a rockslide, other times it sticks. The original summit can end up lower than the fracture crest.

These split ridges are most common in slabby or slaty rocks with deeply-penetrating joints or cleavage planes. In the Alps, doppelgrats can easily run for a kilometre or more, with 'secret' internal valleys perhaps a hundred metres deep. They are prized for the shelter they give livestock, sometimes with grassy floors for summer grazings – even with field names. They are equally valued by walkers and ski-mountaineers, affording safe and speedy travel along ranges where the crests may be spiky and treacherous.

Hardly anyone knows that Scotland has a few – our mountains may not reach as high as the Alps, but they do start from sea level. And we certainly have a lot of the right kind of rock – the metamorphic schists. Of course, our doppelgrats are more modest. In Lochaber, there is one between the summits of Gulvain in

Aonach Sgoilte

Looking up Gleann an Dubh-Lochain

Aonach
Sgoilte
doppelgrat
Ladhar
Bheinn

sagged
slopes
main
antiscarp

Mam
Barrisdale

Lochiel, and a fine example on Sgùrr Chòinnich Mòr in the Grey Corries.

Scarcely anyone realises that by far the grandest, a doppelgrat of Alpine scale, can be found on Knoydart. You couldn't fatten one lamb in it, but you could ski through it in a good winter.

From above Inverie, a great mountain ridge rises eastwards to culminate in Ladhar Bheinn. If you get up onto it above Loch an Dubh-Lochain, you will soon come to Aonach Sgoilte. It is aptly named because the Gaelic name means 'split ridge'. It is not obvious what is happening at first, but gradually you are drawn into a defile between two rocky ribs. Climb the one on the north side, go out along its airy crest, and you end up above a long drop into Coire Torr an Asgaill. This is the lower rib, but at least it's solid ground. Now climb the higher one, with its 758m summit. Quickly carry on down to a narrow col and on up the main ridge. Look back and you see the scene in the upper picture on the opposite page – that robust rocky summit has clearly slipped down a good 10–15 metres. And stopped. For now.

We weren't there to see it move – that probably took centuries some 10,000 years ago – after the glaciers of the last ice age had melted away – but we are pretty confident that it did. For if you drop off south into Gleann an Dubh-Lochain, you will find evidence of landslipping almost all the way to the foot. One remarkable tell-tale sign crosses the midslopes for 500 metres. The slope has ruptured, bursting out with a steep 'antiscarp' facing uphill. It is one of the biggest in Scotland, almost 8 metres high.

Now it's easier to understand what was going on up top. From the summit of Aonach Sgoilte, going back towards Inverie, the deep fracture trench soon fades out. Here two wedge-shaped scars bite into the ridge, where great chunks have slipped south. The fracture reappears some 30 metres down the north face, with its 5 metre high parapet marking where the whole mountain has begun slipping south; it gradually dwindles into a furrow. All in all, this Knoydart ridge is splitting asunder for a distance of about 1.5 kilometres. And all because a glacier from the inland ice cap came scouring over Màm Barrisdale, excavated the glen, and destabilised the whole mountainside.

Blockfield on the Island of Rum

Noel Williams

A distant view of Bloodstone Hill with Canna behind

Looking across to the Rum Cuillin from Orval

A distant view of the Rum Cuillin from Sròn an t-Saighdeir

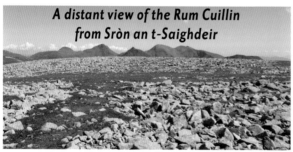

Blockfield on the summit of Sròn an t-Saighdeir

If you venture onto the local mountains you'll notice that the ground underfoot varies markedly from boggy peat to bare rocky ridges. The character of the terrain largely depends upon the nature of the underlying rock and how it has been affected by recent glaciations.

Mainland Scotland was probably completely covered by ice during the last major glacial episode, when ice extended as far south as the English midlands. The scraping action of the ice caused much of the landscape to be swept clean.

However, during the most recent, short-lived glacial episode some 12,000 years ago a much smaller ice cap developed over the Scottish Highlands and many of the highest summits remained above the ice as features called 'nunataks' – named after similar peaks seen today in Greenland.

These summits, although not covered by ice, were subjected to prolonged freeze-thaw action. They experienced what geologists call periglacial conditions. On some mountains, such as Ben Nevis and Ben Alder for example, this created extensive areas of boulders known as **blockfield** (also called felsenmeer – a German word meaning 'sea of rock').

Exactly why these blocks are created on some rocks and not others is still a bit of a mystery. They seem to be best developed in brittle rocks with widely spaced cracks or joints such as quartzite and microgranite.

The island of Rum is particularly fascinating to geologists because exposed in the Rum Cuillin is the remains of a magma chamber which once fed a huge volcano. The very different western hills of Rum are just as fascinating, but for a different reason. They have some of the best periglacial features seen in Scotland.

During the last glacial episode eleven separate glaciers are though to have formed on Rum. Nine of these developed in the Rum Cuillin and two in the western hills on the northern flanks of Sron an t-Saighdeir.

Much of western Rum is made of granitic rock (microgranite and granophyre). It is on this rock that the best examples of periglacial features are found. The summits of Sron an t-Saighdeir and Ard Nev have extensive areas of blockfield.

In stark contrast the neighbouring summits of Bloodstone Hill and Orval have a pleasant covering of grass. This is because the summits of these hills are made of basalt lavas – the same lavas that form the neighbouring island of Canna.

On the flanks of the granitic hills the ground is covered by blockslopes and boulder lobes where the bouldery debris has moved down hill. This movement occurred when the ground thawed out and became waterlogged during milder summer conditions.

Other periglacial features developed on these western hills include stone circles and stone stripes. It is thought that some of these features are still being formed on a smaller scale at the present day.

If you'd like to learn more about some of the periglacial features found on Rum, look out for a booklet called *Rum and the Small Isles – a Landscape Fashioned by Geology* published by Scottish Natural Heritage.

Looking across to Orval from the north flank of Sron an t-Saighdeir. There was a glacier in the intervening corrie some 12,000 years ago.

The Rum Cuillin – an exposed magma chamber

Alison Austin

We return to Rum in this article to look at the spectacular scenery in the central and eastern part of the island. The mountains here are known as the Rum Cuillin and are very popular with hillwalkers. Climbers too are attracted by the largest mass of **peridotite** rock found in Britain – 'the best rock in the world for climbing on'.

However, the rocks forming the Rum Cuillin also have an amazing story to tell. They have been closely studied by geologists from around the world and are one of the reasons why Lochaber has been awarded European and Global Geopark status.

A traverse of the Rum Cuillin makes a superb day out, but even when you just view these mountains from the ferry as you approach the island you can see that they tower over the rest of the Small Isles. Why should that be? Well it's all to do with Rum's fiery past.

Around 60 million years ago things started to get violent – volcanically speaking that is! All along the western coast of Scotland lava poured out from long fissures in the Earth's crust. This was when Greenland started to separate from Europe and eventually gave rise to the North Atlantic Ocean. Today volcanic eruptions along the Mid-Atlantic ridge continue to create new ocean floor and push Scotland and Greenland further apart by around 2 cm each year – about the same speed as your fingernails grow.

On Rum molten rock or magma started to rise in the Earth's crust and dome up the existing rocks (mainly Torridonian sandstones). It eventually caused the collapse of a huge

Climbing on PERIDOTITE on the south face of Barkeval

caldera 10km across. In a cataclysmic event – which was probably ten times larger than that which occurred on Mount St Helens in 1980 – hot ash and fragments of rock were blasted out of a volcano in a series of devastating eruptions of scalding gas and debris known as pyroclastic flows. Some of the magma remained in the magma chamber, however, and eventually cooled to form granite. The peaks of Ard Nev and Orval in the far west of Rum are made of this pink rock.

After the initial eruptions, different magma was injected into the magma chamber from deeper down in the earth. As this magma started to cool different minerals crystallised at different temperatures and settled to the bottom of the chamber as two distinct layers. Another influx of magma took place, and the process was repeated again and again, so building up an impressive series of alternating layers of 'soft' peridotite and 'hard' gabbro.

This created what is known as a layered intrusion and accounts for the distinctive stepped profile of the mountains Hallival and Askival. In fact the ring of peaks which overlook the Atlantic ocean (Barkeval, Hallival, Askival and Trollaval) are all part of what is regarded as a 'staggeringly impressive' world class example of a layered intrusion.

Although none of the lavas from the actual volcano on Rum have been preserved, there are remnants of lava flows in western Rum, Eigg, Canna and Muck that can be linked to huge volcanoes centred on Skye and Mull. These lava flows are made up of a dark coloured fine-grained rock called basalt.

The layered rocks high on the Rum Cuillin hide another secret. They are the reason why the island is host to one of the world's largest breeding colonies of the rare Manx shearwater. These nocturnal birds dig their burrows in the softer peridotite layers between the gabbro layers on Hallival, Askival and Trollaval.

To learn more about the Rum Cuillin see an SNH booklet entitled *Rum and the Small Isles – a Landscape Fashioned by Geology*.

Hallival (L) and Askival (R) viewed from Barkeval

Mile Dorcha – The Dark Mile

Noel Williams

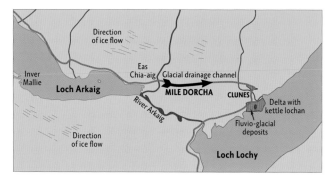

If you follow the B8005 road from Gairlochy via the tiny community of Clunes to the north shore of Loch Arkaig you pass through a sombre little glen known as the *Mile Dorcha* or Dark Mile. Bonnie Prince Charlie rode on horseback down the west side of Loch Lochy and through the Dark Mile on 17th April 1746 – the day after the battle of Culloden. After spending time on the Outer Isles, Skye and wandering over vast tracts of the Western Highlands he returned to this area in the second half of August before eventually escaping to France in September of the same year. The Prince is believed to have stayed in a cave high on the hillside on the north side of the Dark Mile. On old maps there is also a mention of 'Prince Charlie's Tree (site of)' in the Dark Mile itself.

One of the most remarkable features of the Dark Mile is the extraordinary coating of moss on the ground and also on the stone wall which runs along its southern side. At the far end of the Dark Mile you arrive at the very picturesque waterfalls known as the *Eas Chia-aig* (Water of the Old Witch) where legend has it that a witch, thought to be responsible for making Cameron of Locheil's cattle ill, was chased and drowned.

If you pass along the first section of road beside Loch Arkaig you will see a small island in the loch covered in trees. A century ago ospreys used to nest here. The island also has the remains of a very ancient vitrified wall or fort structure as well as a ruined chapel.

There is also more recent history associated with Achnacarry where the Commandos trained in the last war.

So what has all this got to do with landscape? If you

The start of the Dark Mile looking west from Clunes

32

decide to buy a geological map of the Loch Lochy area [Sheet 62 (E)] you will discover that there are two different sorts of map available. One is called a 'Bedrock' map the other is a 'Superficial' map. The Bedrock (or 'Solid') map indicates the solid rock beneath the soil, which to the west of the Great Glen is mainly very old metamorphosed sandstone or psammite. The Superficial (or 'Drift') map shows the material lying on top of the bedrock – such as moraine and peat. It also shows special symbols marking various glacial features. A simple red line is used to mark features indicating the direction of ice movement which at the eastern end of Loch Arkaig is generally towards the east-south-east. Another symbol used is a thick black arrow

Stone wall covered in luxuriant moss

which indicates a glacial drainage channel. One of these arrows runs from west to east along the Dark Mile.

This tells us that when the glacier which filled the Loch Arkaig basin started to melt some 11,500 years ago much of the water from it poured through the Dark Mile and into the Great Glen. Important evidence for this can be seen nearby on the western shore of Loch Lochy. Immediately south of Clunes

there is a small delta and kettle lochan where material was deposited by this torrent of meltwater. The delta is marked as *Blàr an Lochain* on OS maps.

There are several other glacial drainage channels marked on the Loch Lochy sheet. One of these is in Leanachan Forest just east of the lime quarry (Grid Ref 190 780), but it does not have the romantic setting of the one along the Dark Mile.

Eas Chia-aig

Strontian – an industrial landscape

Ian Parsons

The Lochaber village of Strontian, on the shore of Loch Sunart, has a very special claim to fame amongst scientists. It is one of only two settlements in the whole world whose modern name has been given to one of the 92 naturally occurring chemical elements. The other place is Ytterby, near Stockholm in Sweden, which gave its name to the four very rare elements yttrium, erbium, terbium and ytterbium.

Today, Strontian is calm and peaceful, but it was not always so. Events leading to the discovery of the element strontium were turbulent, even brutal. About 1722 the mineral galena, the source of lead, was discovered in veins on a bleak, boggy, rain and windswept hillside some three miles north of the village. Mining commenced in 1725. Miners were brought in from the north of England, where minerals were igniting the industrial revolution, and these incomers were not popular with the locals, who lived a miserable existence of subsistence farming and fishing. A church Minister complained '…of late [have] come…near Three Hundred Miners…who Labour in a Lead Mine. They are a people for the most part of different principals from the Church of Scotland, and the greater part are prophain in their practice'. Dear me! The miners stole horses, cattle and tools, and committed acts of vandalism. Many were housed in a shanty town called New York (so named, no doubt, to capture the excitement of a British colony far away). Mining supplies and food had to be brought in by sea, and when this failed miners died of starvation. In 1745 Bonny Prince Charlie was joined by local men who stole gunpowder from the mines. The English response was to send the Royal Navy, closing the sea-lanes and preventing stores reaching Strontian, leading to widespread starvation. Flooding following the frequent heavy rain was a constant problem. A water-powered pump was installed in 1757, but it stopped working in 1758 following a 5-month drought, and after further flooding the mines closed in 1760.

In 1764 a man of the kirk, the Rev. Dr John Walker, visited the derelict mines. Walker, known as 'the mad Minister of Moffat', had an insatiable appetite for natural history specimens and was on a six-month collecting tour of the Highlands and Hebrides. He discovered a mineral (later called strontianite) that he recognised had a distinctive appearance and properties. In 1790 an Irish physician, Adair Crawford, suggested it contained a new 'earth' (the oxide, strontia), and this was confirmed by careful experiments in 1793 by Thomas Hope, who later became a professor at Edinburgh University. The metallic element strontium was eventually extracted from strontianite (strontium carbonate) in 1808 by the great chemist (and inventor of the miner's lamp) Sir Humphry Davy, who visited Strontian and stayed below Whitesmith mine, at Bellgrove Lodge. The ore veins have yielded many fine mineral specimens, including the first examples of another strontium-bearing mineral, brewsterite, named after a distinguished Scottish chemist, Sir David Brewster, who also invented the kaleidoscope.

The Strontian main vein

Short-lived and financially unsuccessful attempts to revitalise the mines continued until the early 1980s, when barite was extracted for the newly-arrived North Sea oil industry, but much larger deposits were soon found elsewhere in Scotland. Today, the activities of miners over nearly three hundred years are mainly recorded by deep clefts where they toiled under dreadful conditions. In the words of one of my sources: 'Strontian was left with industrial scars on an already barren landscape, and a name enshrined in the Periodic Table...'

This article drew on a variety of sources, but I am particularly grateful for historical nuggets provided by Jim Kirby of Polloch.

Needles of strontianite, strontium carbonate

Flood Basalts or Plateau Lavas   *Jim Blair*

About 60 million years ago, Lochaber, especially the western part, would not have been a very pleasant place to be, unless you liked living dangerously!

At that time, the North Atlantic had not yet opened up to become the ocean that we are familiar with today; and Greenland was just over our north-western horizon. As the process of rifting began long cracks, or fissures developed in the Earth's crust. Hot, basaltic lava spewed out of these fissures onto the land surface in a massive volcanic outburst, which extended from Antrim in Northern Ireland, up the west coast of Scotland and northwards towards Shetland.

The basaltic lava was very fluid because of its particular chemical composition and high temperature of over 1,000 °C. Rather than build a classic, conical volcanic mountain, the lava flowed away from the fissures and filled in all the hollows and valleys in the landscape. Layer upon layer of basalt lava 'flooded' across the land, forming near-horizontal sheets of hard basalt rock and in some places completely 'drowning out' the previous landscape.

There were sometimes long intervals between eruptions, and this gave time for the surface of the lava to weather and break down to form soil. Plants and even large trees grew in this soil until they were swamped and buried by the next flood of lava.

The landscape created by these flood basalts has a distinctive terraced or stair-like, stepped appearance. This is sometimes called 'trap' scenery, from the Dutch or Swedish word for a staircase. Each terrace represents a separate lava flow and on average is about 15m (50ft) thick. Within Lochaber, some

Canna seen from Rum

Ardtornish

of the best flood basalts can be seen in Morvern on either side of Loch Aline, and also in the northern part of the island of Eigg.

Continental flood basalt eruptions are the largest known eruptions of lava on Earth. Individual flows can exceed 2000 cubic kilometres in volume. The final pile of lavas can extend over an area of more than a million square kilometres. Two particularly spectacular events in the geological past created the Deccan Traps in western India (65 million years ago) and the Siberian Traps in Russia (250 million years ago). It has even been suggested that when these phenomenal quantities of lava were erupted the huge quantities of gas added to the atmosphere may have contributed to mass extinctions of life on Earth.

Some geologists think that all this volcanic activity is linked to the formation of huge blobs of hot molten rock, called 'mantle plumes', which rise up under the

Looking south-west from the road to Rahoy

Earth's crust, and dome it upwards. When fissures develop in the overlying crust the pressure on the plume is released and lava bursts out. Iceland is believed to be sitting over a mantle plume at the present day.

The whole volcanic episode on the west coast of Scotland lasted for some 5 million years. More than fifty million years of erosion have since removed a huge proportion of the original flood basalts. However, we can still see the remains of lava flows today on Mull, Ardnamurchan,

the Small Isles of Rum, Eigg, Canna and Muck, as well as on Skye and the Shiant Isles. Some of these lavas developed hexagonal columns when they cooled.

When the flood basalt stage had finished, volcanic activity became concentrated for a while around more localised centres on Ardnamurchan, Rum, Mull, and Skye, each forming major volcanic complexes. These have been studied by geologists for over a hundred years and are still the object of detailed research today.

An Steall – a classic hanging valley
Noel Williams

One of the most popular outings in the Fort William area is the walk from the top car park in Glen Nevis through the Nevis Gorge to visit the spectacular waterfall called An Steall. Glen Nevis is arguably the most beautiful and varied glen in Scotland, and it is no wonder that this outing is so popular. What is not so widely known is that there are three different routes through the Nevis Gorge on its eastern flank.

By far the most popular route is the middle path, but in places this has shear drops down to the Water of Nevis below and it is advisable to stay well clear of the edge. The lower path is even scarier as it is very narrow in places and also has shear drops down to the jumble of giant boulders in the riverbed below. The upper path climbs well above the gorge and is beautifully engineered. It gives superb views of the whole glen and is by far the safest of the routes through to An Steall. Unfortunately the start of this upper path is very difficult to recognise. It cuts off on the left where the middle path curves rightwards about 100m after crossing a small stream by a gangway cut in red granite.

Whichever route is taken to An Steall the change in character of the glen on reaching the flat floor beyond the gorge is truly dramatic. If you look carefully at the crags immediately above the path at this point you may be able to see smooth-sided cavities in the rock. These are parts of potholes created by water cascading down the margin of the glacier which once filled the glen in the last Ice Age.

The spectacular waterfall of An Steall itself is straight

Looking along the Nevis Gorge to An Steall with the mountain of An Gearanach behind

1 Leven Schists (youngest)
2 Glen Coe Quartzite
3 Binnein Schists (oldest)

An Steall

ahead. The Gaelic name An Steall means 'The Cataract'. It is commonly called Steall Waterfall, but this name is a bit of a nonsense because that is the same as saying 'Waterfall Waterfall'.

The water spilling out of Coire a' Mhail crashes down over 120m (400ft) of quartzite strata to reach the floor of Glen Nevis. Coire a' Mhail is a classic example of a hanging valley. It was created when the large glacier in Glen Nevis cut down deeply into the local bedrock and left steep flanks and a U-shaped profile. The smaller side glacier in Coire a' Mhail did not erode as deeply and the corrie has been left 'hanging' above the main glen. It is rather like a miniature version of Bridalveil Falls in Yosemite.

An Steall is not the biggest waterfall in the UK (that title goes to Eas a' Chual Aluinn in Sutherland), but it is certainly one of the most scenic.

However there is another story behind the formation of this extraordinary feature. The water cascades over layers of a rock called Glen Coe Quartzite. The same rock also forms the Grey Corries ridge and the summits of several local mountains such as the Pap of Glencoe, Stob Ban and Sgurr a' Mhaim.

You will notice that An Steall cascades over layers of quartzite which dip down to the right. However just a little

bit further up Glen Nevis the same strata are seen to be folded completely back on themselves. Indeed the same strata seen in An Steall then curve back rightwards to form the summit of mighty Sgurr a' Mhaim (1099m). This is a marvellous example of what geologists call a recumbent fold. How is it that solid rocks have been folded on such a scale?

Well, around 450 million years ago when these rocks formed the roots of the Caledonian Mountain Chain they were buried some 20km below the surface. They were so hot at that depth that when they were squeezed between two colliding plates in the Earth's crust they behaved like plasticine. As a result of this great squeezing the rocks now forming the Mamores have not only been metamorphosed but they have also been turned completely upside down.

The white quartzite rocks forming the summit of Sgùrr a' Mhaim have been turned completely upside down.

Loch Morar – Britain's deepest loch

Noel Williams

Looking across Mointeach Mhòr to Eigg and Rum

Loch Morar

The River Morar

The west coast of Scotland has a remarkably indented coastline which is characterised by long, deep sea lochs or fjords. These fjords were excavated by glaciers which flowed westwards from the large ice sheet which built up over mainland Scotland on a number of occasions during the last Ice Age. The east coast of Greenland and the west coast of Norway both have very similar types of coastline. Hornindalsvatnet in Norway is the deepest freshwater loch (514m) in Europe.

When a bathymetric survey of Scottish freshwater lochs was carried out a century ago the floor of Loch Morar was found to be 310m deep. This makes it easily the deepest freshwater loch in Britain. The next deepest is Loch Ness at 230m. To achieve these sorts of depths the pre-existing river valleys must have been scooped out by large and relatively fast flowing glaciers. In the case of Loch Ness the glaciers took advantage of the shattered belt of weaker rocks formed along the line of the Great Glen Fault. Several

Looking across Loch Morar towards the mountains of Knoydart

of the freshwater lochs in Lochaber run in an east-west direction – these include Loch Morar, Loch Arkaig, Loch Eilt and Loch Beoraid – but strangely no major faults have been identified to account for this alignment.

The surface of Loch Morar is only some 10m above present day sea level. So the floor of Loch Morar lies well below sea level. Indeed you have to go beyond St Kilda before the sea bed is generally deeper than this. The deepest feature on the British Continental Shelf is the 300m deep trench in the Inner Sound of Raasay.

The last major ice sheet to cover Scotland began to melt rapidly around 17,000 years ago. Sea level was for a while some 40m higher than it is today relative to the land surface in the Arisaig area. So there is little doubt that for a time at least Loch Morar was a sea loch. The main link with the sea would have been across what is now Mointeach Mhor. This is the flat boggy moorland just north of Arisaig where the new road was built a few years ago. However, huge quantities of sand and gravel were swept along by the meltwater from the main ice sheet. This choked up Loch Morar's former link with the sea at its south-western end. A similar situation almost happened much further south with Loch Etive. However, a channel remained open through the outwash material which forms the Moss of Achnacree at North Connel, and Loch Etive is still linked to the sea.

When world wide sea levels started to more or less stabilise some 5,000 years ago the land continued to 'bounce' back up after its burden of ice had been removed. This is when the water trapped in Loch Morar started to escape further north. A small hydro-electric station has been built to harness the energy from the very short but fast flowing River Morar. A tiny stream called the Allt Cam Carach, which originates near a bay at the western end of Loch Morar, called Camas Ruadh, still flows across Mointeach Mhor to reach the sea near Back of Keppoch. But this sluggish stream is no longer a competitor for the River Morar.

The Arisaig area has one of the world's finest records of changing sea level since the last major glaciation. Research is continuing to unravel the timing of these dramatic events.

Darwin and Lochaber

Keith Hoole

The year 2009 marked not only the bicentenary of Charles Darwin's birth in 1809, but also 150 years since the publication of his hugely influential book *On The Origin of Species*. What is perhaps not so widely known is the connection that Darwin has with Lochaber. Darwin developed an interest in geology at the very end of his studies as a divinity student in Cambridge following an outing in North Wales with one of the pre-eminent geologists of the day, Professor Adam Sedgwick. The Sedgwick name now graces the Earth Science museum in Cambridge. It is also familiar in Lochaber as our local surgeon proudly counts the Professor as one of his antecedents.

On his return from his outing with Sedgwick Darwin learnt that 'Captain Fitz-Roy was willing to give up part of his own cabin to any young man who would volunteer to go with him without pay as naturalist to the Voyage of the Beagle.' He nearly failed the interview:

'Afterwards on becoming very intimate with Fitz-Roy, I heard that I had run a very narrow risk of being rejected, on account of the shape of my nose! He ... was convinced that he could judge a man's character by the outline of his features; and he doubted whether anyone with my nose could possess sufficient energy and determination for the voyage. But I think he was afterwards well-satisfied that my nose had spoken falsely.'

On the Beagle voyage (1831-6) Darwin had with him a copy of *Principles of Geology* by the Scottish-born geologist Charles Lyell, and he took a keen interest in geological features throughout his travels. It was following his voyage around the world in HMS Beagle that Charles Darwin made his name as an outstanding natural scientist. Lyell later

A drawing of Charles Darwin made in 1840 by George Richmond
© English Heritage Photo Library

became a great friend and supporter.

Charles Darwin's connection with Lochaber was through the 'Parallel Roads' of Glen Roy. Darwin came to Glen Roy in June 1838 to examine these famous hillside markings. Only a few years before he had seen conspicuous raised beaches in South America. This no doubt influenced his thinking for he concluded that the 'Roads' in Glen Roy were marine beaches which had formed when the Scottish landmass rose from the sea in a series of steps. Darwin walked the 'Parallel Roads' looking for fragments of sea shells, but failed to find any.

Despite the final outcome of these studies, it is interesting to read of Darwin's visit to Lochaber in his own words in a letter he sent to Charles Lyell:

'I crossed from Edinburgh in gigs & carts, (& carts without springs as I never shall forget) ... & reached Glen Roy on Saturday evening... Here I enjoyed five days of the most beautiful weather, with gorgeous sunsets, & all nature looking as happy, as I felt.–I wandered over the mountains in all directions & examined that most extraordinary district.–I think without any exception,–not even the first volcanic island, the first elevated beach, or the passage of the Cordillera, was so interesting to me, as this week. It is far the most remarkable area I ever examined. ... I can assure you Glen Roy has astonished me.'

Then, in 1840, Louis Agassiz paid a visit to Glen Roy. What he saw convinced him that the various 'Roads' in Lochaber were the shorelines of freshwater lochs created when glaciers blocked the normal exits from the glens. This was eventually recognised as the correct explanation, but it was revolutionary at that time, because few people then believed that glaciers had ever existed in Britain.

Darwin did not finally abandon his marine theory until 1861 when Scottish geologist Thomas Francis Jamieson (with the support of Darwin and Lyell) visited Glen Roy. Jamieson put forward a clear sequence of events, involving glacial advance and retreat, which is still regarded as the correct explanation for the formation of these famous features.

This prompted Darwin to confess to Lyell:

'I am smashed to atoms about Glen Roy. My paper was one long gigantic blunder from beginning to end.'

Darwin may have had to eat humble pie over Glen Roy, but this was of little consequence when measured against the importance of his ideas on natural selection which had been launched on the world in 1859.

On one of the Parallel Roads in Glen Roy with all three roads visible on the hillside behind

Earthquakes in Lochaber

Julian Bukits – British Geological Survey, Edinburgh

The district of Lochaber is situated in the middle of a seismically active area of northwest Scotland, which extends roughly 300 km from Arran in the south to Ullapool in the north. This is one of the UK's five main areas of earthquake activity.

Since the British Geological Survey (BGS) started a monitoring programme in the early 1970s, approximately 350 earthquakes have been recorded in the Lochaber area. Around 80% are small, with magnitudes of less than 2.0, and go unnoticed by the general public, partly because of their small size and partly because they often occur in remote areas. However, the

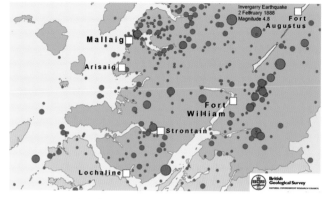

Earthquake Magnitude	
●	4.0–4.9
●	3.0–3.9
●	2.0–2.9
·	<2.0

● Historical events (pre-1970)

◉ Instrumental recordings

tiny vibrations from such earthquakes can be recorded by sensitive instruments called seismometers and used to build up an accurate picture of earthquake activity.

Since 1972, there have also been ten earthquakes in Lochaber with magnitudes of between 3.0 and 3.7. Earthquakes of this size are largely observed by the local population, especially if they are indoors where windows, doors and household effects may rattle and hanging objects may swing. They can also awaken people from sleep. Although people indoors may feel such earthquakes, those outdoors are much less likely to, mainly because they are busy doing something and won't be aware of the small clues that an earthquake has occurred.

Most recently a magnitude 3.5 earthquake struck Glenfinnan on 10 October

Seismometers

2008. The earthquake was widely felt by residents of Glenfinnan, Fort William, Ardgour and Strontian, and as far away as Mallaig and Drumnadrochit. The BGS used an online questionnaire to gather information from members of the public, receiving over 200 replies. Although the strength of the shaking was only moderate, lasting between 2-3 seconds, it was strong enough to make furniture shake and windows or crockery rattle. Most reports indicated that people were woken from their sleep and of a few being frightened. People described the earthquake as being like "a train rumbling past" and that the "dogs also went mad barking and growling".

Prior to the 1970s, evidence for earthquake activity can be gathered from local newspapers and historical archives. In the Lochaber area there is evidence of at least fifteen such earthquakes. Significantly, there have been five events recorded with magnitudes estimated at greater than 4.0. The largest of these events occurred near Invergarry on 2nd February 1888 and had an estimated magnitude of 4.8. Although this was a relatively large earthquake by Scottish standards, little damage was reported as the epicentre was in a remote mountainous

area. However, there were some cases of damage to plaster in Fort William. The shock was felt across a large part of Scotland, including Edinburgh and Glasgow to the south, Thurso in the north and the Hebrides to the west. It is also recorded that the event was preceded by two small foreshocks and a long, well-documented series of aftershocks that lasted up until 1899.

What is remarkable about the pattern of earthquake activity across the Highlands is the lack of a match with the location of major faults. Important structural boundaries such as the Great Glen fault do not seem to correspond with any increased incidence of earthquake activity nor do they mark dividing lines between zones of differing rates of seismicity.

It seems likely that the pattern of seismicity may be influenced by something completely different – the distribution of ice during the last glaciation. Most of the earthquakes occur in the western half of the country. The last ice cap to form over Scotland extended from Torridon in the north to the Trossachs in the south. It formed where precipitation was greatest – over western hills. The eastern hills remained largely ice-free. The western hills were depressed by their burden of ice, and when the ice eventually started to melt they began to 'bounce back up again' – by a process geologists term isostatic rebound. That process is still going on today.

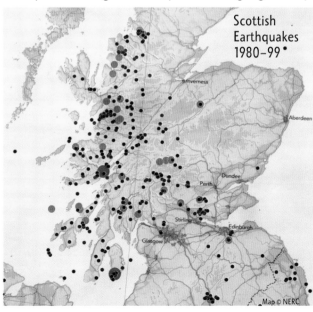

Scottish Earthquakes 1980–99 •

Map © NERC

The latest discoveries about the Parallel Roads

Adrian Palmer, Royal Holloway, University of London

The Lochaber district provides important insights into our recent glacial history, with the Parallel Roads of Glen Roy playing a unique role. The Roads we see today must have developed during the most recent glacial phase, because any earlier ones would have been destroyed when ice cover was more extensive. Brian Sissons of the University of Edinburgh mapped the local evidence in great detail during the 1970s, refining their probable age to around 12,000 years ago. He also concluded that the lakes had drained catastrophically by a series of enormous floods, the biggest of which swept down the Great Glen into Loch Ness because the waters could not escape into Loch Linnhe, which was still occupied by ice. Dislocations of the roads also suggest that the region experienced major earthquakes and landslips at this time, caused by sudden changes in the volume (and hence weight) of the glaciers and lake waters.

More recently, scientists from the Department of Geography, Royal Holloway, University of London, have identified **varves** – fine-grained lake sediments composed of tiny individual annual layers. These imply that each lake stood at its respective shoreline for between 100 and 200 years, and that the total period during which the lakes existed was 500 years. This in turn also defines the period during which the glaciers advanced into and receded from Glen Spean, indicating just how quickly these processes can operate. One wonders how Darwin might have reacted to such radical revisions of our ideas on rates of environmental change.

Left: a recent field outing in Glen Roy. Above: a close up of the lake sediments showing coarser layers deposited in summer alternating with finer layers deposited in winter.